REFLECTING GOD

JOURNAL

Kay Smith

THE WORD
FOR TODAY

P.O. Box 8000, Costa Mesa, CA 92628 • Web Site: www.twft.com • E-mail: info@twft.com

Reflecting God Journal

Published by The Word For Today
P.O. Box 8000, Costa Mesa, CA 92628

Web site: www.twft.com
(800) 272-WORD (9673)

© 2009 The Word For Today

ISBN: 978-1-59751-094-3

Unless otherwise indicated, Scripture quotations in this book are taken from the New King James Version of the Bible. Copyright © 1979, 1980, 1982 by Thomas Nelson, Inc., Publishers. Used by permission. Translational emendations, amplifications, and paraphrases are by the author.

Printed in the United States of America.

FOREWORD

The *Reflecting God Journal* is designed to accompany *Reflecting God*, the book written by Kay Smith. Each question can be answered by referring to the text in the *Reflecting God* book and by reading the scriptural references stated within.

This study can be done in a variety of ways. Small weekly groups are ideal for discussion, prayer, and fellowship. The *Reflecting God* book and journal can also be used as an individual study tool and devotion time for personal growth.

To get the most of this study:

MAKE TIME.

If possible, set aside a specific time each day to do your study. Consistency is key. Since our busy lives can make it difficult to spend time with the Lord, we need to make sure we give Him a portion of our day to hear from Him.

PRAY.

Ask the Holy Spirit to open your eyes and your heart to behold the wondrous things in His Word. Pray that the truths you learn will be applied to your life and worked out in your attitude and actions.

READ.

Each day, read the assigned portions and meditate on the Scripture to see what the Lord would say to your heart. Be sure to memorize key verses.

STUDY.

You can use other available tools in your study, such as various Bible translations, dictionaries, concordances, and commentaries for further research and insight. However, the best commentary of all is the Holy Spirit.

APPLY.

God has given us a manual for living a life that reflects Him. If we apply the truths we learn, we can have a victorious Christian walk. Application is the key to getting the most from this study.

ATTEND.

If you are doing this study in a group setting, be sure to diligently attend and participate in the discussions and fellowship. If you are new to studying the Bible, don't be concerned if you can't answer every question. You will learn and be encouraged just from hearing other women's answers and experiences.

GROUP LEADER GUIDELINES

As a group leader, your responsibility is not to teach but to:

• Encourage discussion.

• Listen and respond appropriately.

• Facilitate conversation flow and a comfortable atmosphere.

• Clarify any confusing questions or contributions by group members.

• Reduce tension through Spirit-led responses and be ready to mediate any conflict.

• Try to promote participation from every group member, averting one person from monopolizing the conversation.

CHAPTER

1

SHE IS THE KING'S DAUGHTER

1. If you belong to Jesus, you're the daughter of the King. As you meditate upon Psalm 45:13, consider how you can reflect the King to those around you.

    _____

    _____

    _____

    _____

2. Read Colossians 3:8-14. What garments should the King's daughter wear? What garments should she put off?

    _____   _____

    _____   _____

    _____   _____

    _____   _____

3. As the King's daughter, you no longer behave as a worldly woman. What should be your conduct? See Ephesians 4:20-24 for this appropriate etiquette.

_____

_____

_____

_____

4. At the very beginning, when all this trouble with sin began, where did it start for Eve? Where does sin start with you and how does sin mature?

_____

_____

_____

_____

5. Write Ephesians 4:23. Why is it important for the King's daughter to renew her mind moment by moment, considering the world in which she lives?

_____

_____

_____

_____

6. When God's Spirit is living within you, your eyes are open to the source behind the world's entertainment, fashions, laws, and lifestyles. Express your response to this awareness.

_____

_____

_____

_____

7. Once the King's daughter begins to interact with a worldly kingdom, she will be subtly deceived. Read Romans 1:21-22 and write it in your own words.

_____

_____

_____

_____

8. If the King's daughter follows the customs of this worldly kingdom, what will happen to her? Write some of the effects listed in Romans 1:29-31.

_____

_____

_____

_____

9. The effects listed above should terrify the King's daughter. As you read Ephesians 4:19, what is the intention of sin's final result upon you?

_____

_____

_____

_____

10. How can the King's daughter be assured that she will not be duped by this world? Find your answer in 1 Corinthians 2:10-16 and write it here.

_____

_____

_____

_____

11. Once you have the mind of Christ, the Holy Spirit will conform your thinking and transform you into His image. Write this promise found in 2 Peter 1:4.

_____

_____

_____

_____

_____

12. The battle for your mind is not over. The King's daughter will always have to renew the spirit of her mind on a daily basis. Write out James 4:7 and memorize it to help you.

_____

_____

_____

_____

_____

Be renewed in the spirit of your mind; and that you put on the new man which was created according to God, in true righteousness and holiness.

- Ephesians 4:23

_____

_____

_____

_____

_____

_____

_____

_____

_____

_____

_____

_____

_____

_____

_____

_____

_____

_____

Prayers & Notes

CHAPTER

2

SHE IS CLOTHED IN BEAUTY

1. As the King's daughter you have access to God's biblical closet. Choose some nice clothes to wear today. Refer to Colossians 3:12-14 and write down your selections.

_____   _____

_____   _____

_____   _____

_____

2. Take a look at the world's dressing room. Read Colossians 3:8-9 and list the garments you will find there.

_____   _____

_____   _____

_____

3. If you don't know Jesus, God's clothing just won't fit! You can only wear one set of clothes at a time: the world's garments or God's. Why? See 1 Corinthians 2:14.

_____

_____

_____

_____

4. To reflect God's beauty, the Bible teaches that Jesus left the beautiful clothes of heaven to come to earth to wear the painful rags of death. Read Philippians 2:5-8 and write why Jesus did this. See also John 3:16.

_____

_____

_____

_____

5. Read 1 Peter 5:5. What are you to be clothed with at all times? Why is this important to reflect God?

_____

_____

_____

_____

6. Our society teaches us to size one another up to see if we look better than the other person. Read Philippians 2:3 and answer how we are to biblically view someone.

_____

_____

_____

_____

7. There's only one you can compare yourself to—Jesus. Read Isaiah 6:1-5 and jot down your thoughts.

_____

_____

_____

_____

8. Your spiritual clothing is provided by God. Read Isaiah 61:10 and write what spiritual garments and accessories the Lord has set out for you today.

_____

_____

_____

_____

9. God will also include covering for your feet. If you've been walking with a spirit of despair, write what Psalm 18:32-33 says will put a skip in your step.

_____

_____

_____

_____

10. Read Isaiah 61:3. According to this Scripture, when people look at the King's daughter, what kind of reflection will they see?

_____

_____

_____

_____

11. To clothe yourself in qualities of kindness, gentleness and humility, what do you need to do according to 2 Corinthians 10:4-5?

_____

_____

_____

_____

_____

12. A woman's style of fashion usually makes a statement. Now after studying this chapter, how can you reflect Christ by the way you dress? Support your answer with Scripture.

_____

_____

_____

_____

I will greatly rejoice in the LORD. My soul shall be joyful in my God; for He has clothed me with the garments of salvation, He has covered me with the robe of righteousness, as a bridegroom decks himself with ornaments, and as a bride adorns herself with her jewels.

- Isaiah 61:10

Prayers & Notes

Prayers & Notes

3

SHE IS HOLY

1. Compare the world's view of holiness with true holiness as outlined in Titus 2:3-5. Write your observations.

    _____

    _____

    _____

    _____

2. Revelation 4:8 tells us the cherubim and seraphim around God's throne say, "Holy, holy, holy, Lord God Almighty." Read 1 Peter 1:15-16 and state God's commandment for holiness.

    _____

    _____

    _____

    _____

3. Like the transformed woman at the well in John 4:28-29, how does a woman reflect God's holiness when she overflows with Christ's living water?

_____

_____

_____

_____

4. In your own words, how would you describe the woman whose behavior reflects God's holiness?

_____

_____

_____

_____

5. Considering Isaiah 26:3, why is a woman who reflects God's holiness peaceful?

_____

_____

_____

_____

6. The holy woman is fruitful. John 15:5 says if you abide in Jesus, you will bear much fruit. List the ways you can bear fruit.

_____

_____

_____

_____

_____

_____

_____

7. Review 2 Peter 3:11-14. Believing that the world is in the process of being dissolved, how can you be consecrated and holy in your behavior?

_____

_____

_____

_____

8. What is God's call for a woman of holiness? Read 1 Thessalonians 4:1-7 to recognize and affirm the will of God for your life.

_____

_____

_____

_____

9. Discipline and chastening are necessary for a commitment to a life of holiness. As you look at Hebrews 12:10, state the benefits of chastening as it relates to reflecting the holiness of God.

_____

_____

_____

_____

10. Revelation 12:10 describes Satan as being the "accuser of the brethren." Think about what happens when we falsely accuse another person. Why is this unholy behavior?

_____

_____

_____

_____

11. Write why the exhortation in Ephesians 5:18 is essential for a woman of holiness.

_____

_____

_____

_____

12. Drinking wine or alcohol to excess will always lead to embarrassing behavior. What kind of holy behavior will you find in Ephesians 5:19?

_____

_____

_____

_____

13. How might you, as a woman of holiness, be an influence and a teacher of good to others?

_____

_____

_____

_____

14. Share a favorite Scripture from this lesson. As you write it, commit it to memory and apply it to your life.

_____

_____

_____

_____

For God did not call us to uncleanness, but in holiness.

- 1 Thessalonians 4:7

Prayers & Notes

Prayers & Notes

_____

_____

_____

_____

_____

_____

_____

_____

_____

_____

_____

_____

_____

_____

_____

_____

_____

C H A P T E R

4

SHE SOWS
TO THE SPIRIT

1. The Bible often uses gardening as an illustration because we can observe God's laws firsthand through nature. Illustrate one of God's unfailing truths found in Galatians 6:7-8.

_____

_____

_____

_____

2. You are planting seeds every single day—either good seeds or bad. Recall your day yesterday and share what type of seeds you sowed into your mind.

_____

_____

_____

_____

3. Think of an area in your community where Satan is sowing bad seed. Write a prayer asking God to destroy that seed and then pledge to scattering good seed through prayer for that particular place.

_____

_____

_____

_____

4. You can be sure that when you violate God's laws you will reap what you sow—and the pain isn't always limited to you. How could seeds of sin affect others?

_____

_____

_____

_____

5. Seeds of sin are deceiving, but memorizing Scriptures will prevent those seeds from growing. Write Hebrews 3:13 and ask God to imprint it upon your heart.

_____

_____

_____

_____

6. Be aware of God's law of sowing and reaping. Although there are natural consequences to your sins, what remedy has God promised to you in 1 John 1:9?

_____

_____

_____

_____

7. It's so important to be careful about what you sow into your mind. Meditate on the following Scriptures and share what you learn.

   a. Romans 8:5-7

   _____
   _____
   _____
   _____

   b. Philippians 2:5

   _____
   _____
   _____
   _____

   c. Colossians 3:1-2

   _____
   _____
   _____
   _____

8. Your words and actions are reflective of what you've allowed into your mind. Why is discontentment a dangerous seed?

   _____
   _____
   _____
   _____
   _____

9. Galatians 6:8 says if you sow to the flesh you will reap corruption. Examine the works of the flesh found in Galatians 5:19-21 and make a list of those works you want God to uproot from you right now.

_____   _____
_____   _____
_____   _____
_____   _____
_____   _____
_____   _____
_____   _____

10. Galatians 6:8 also promises if you sow to the Spirit you will reap everlasting life. List some ways you can sow to the Spirit.

_____   _____
_____   _____
_____   _____

11. Psalm 126:5-6 offers great hope to continue sowing God's seed, even when you are discouraged. Write this beautiful promise and allow it to grow.

_____
_____
_____
_____

And let us not grow weary while doing good, for in due season we shall reap if we do not lose heart.

- Galatians 6:9

Prayers & Notes

Prayers & Notes

SHE CONTINUALLY GROWS

1. We should always be growing and maturing in the Lord—never allowing ourselves to become dormant. List some things that can cause spiritual dormancy.

_____   _____
_____   _____
_____   _____
_____   _____

2. A woman who reflects God is expected to grow. What does Ephesians 4:14-16 say about spiritual maturity?

_____
_____
_____
_____

3. Matthew 5:48 declares the ultimate goal for spiritual growth. Explain what Jesus means by His statement.

_____

_____

4. Paul described the believers in 1 Corinthians 3:1-3 as spiritual babies. What traits characterized that church? Do you see any of these traits in yourself? If so, pray for the Holy Spirit to help you.

_____

_____

_____

_____

5. If you are totally dependent on others for spiritual counsel, it's very likely you will remain immature in your faith. Look at the following Scriptures and share what you discover.

    a. Isaiah 9:6

_____

_____

    b. John 14:26

_____

_____

    c. 1 Corinthians 2:14-16

_____

_____

_____

_____

6. If you want to grow continually, you will need key nutrients. Much like plants, the first nourishment is good soil. Write what you find in these Scriptures.

   a. Psalm 92:13

   _____

   _____

   b. Ephesians 3:17

   _____

   _____

7. Believers need air, or the right atmosphere, in order to grow. What atmosphere is vital for your spiritual growth? Refer to Hebrews 10:24-25.

   _____

   _____

   _____

8. Light is very important for spiritual growth. What do you discover about light from these Scriptures?

   a. Psalm 119:105, 130

   _____

   _____

   _____

   b. John 8:12

   _____

   _____

9. Water will always promote continual growth. List some ways God's living water ministers to us through these Bible verses.

a. John 4:13-14

_____

_____

b. Ephesians 5:26

_____

_____

10. Some Christians stop growing when adversity comes. What do you learn in Romans 8:28-29 about God's ultimate purpose in trials?

_____

_____

_____

11. Are you or someone you know in the midst of difficult circumstances today? Write a prayer asking the Lord to help you or your friend grow and mature through this suffering.

_____

_____

_____

_____

_____

Be perfect as your Father in heaven is perfect, that is, grow into complete maturity of godliness in mind and character.

- Matthew 5:48

Prayers & Notes

Prayers & Notes

CHAPTER

6

SHE IS JOYFUL
IN TRIALS

1. Your attitude towards life has everything to do with reflecting God. Take a moment and really think about your attitude right now and write your comments.

_____

_____

_____

_____

_____

2. No one is immune from trials or difficulties. According to James 1:2, what should be your mindset as you face hardships?

_____

_____

_____

3. Read Hebrews 12:2 and reflect upon the suffering Jesus endured upon the cross. What was His attitude and how was He able to have this frame of mind?

_____
_____
_____
_____

4. When trials appear unexpectedly, you can grow better or bitter. What are the pressures in your life forming in you right now? If there is bitterness, confess it to the Lord and allow Him to remove it from your heart.

_____
_____
_____
_____

5. Philippians 4:6 reminds us to pray with an attitude of gratitude. Record a time when God has answered your prayer, met your need, or even performed a miracle in your life.

_____
_____
_____
_____

6. Read Exodus 17:1-7. How can these verses minister to you today to have a thankful heart?

_____
_____
_____
_____

7. As you write Psalm 30:5, share how this beautiful promise will help you to count it all joy—no matter what things look like at the moment.

_____

_____

_____

_____

8. Just as gold is purified through fire, so are you purified through trials. What impurities do you think the Lord is cleansing from your life right now?

_____

_____

_____

_____

9. God wants to do a work in your life and a trial is simply an instrument to accomplish His purpose. See James 1:3-4 to find the purpose of trials. Write it here.

_____

_____

_____

_____

10. As difficult as your trials may be right now, what does the Lord promise you in James 1:12?

_____

_____

_____

_____

11. First Peter 1:6-7 explains why you can greatly rejoice in the midst of your trials. Write this assurance.

_____

_____

_____

_____

12. After reading 1 Peter 4:12-14, what do you learn:

a. About trials?

_____

_____

b. Why you are to rejoice?

_____

_____

c. How you can have joy?

_____

_____

My brethren, count it all joy when you fall into various trials, knowing that the testing of your faith produces patience. But let patience have its perfect work, that you may be perfect and complete, lacking nothing.

- James 1:4

Prayers & Notes

_____

_____

_____

_____

_____

_____

_____

_____

_____

_____

_____

_____

_____

_____

_____

_____

_____

_____

_____

Prayers & Notes

SHE IS
LOVING

1. Jesus had spoken to His disciples often about the
    one quality by which the world would judge their
    discipleship—*agape* love. Paraphrase John 13:34-35.

    _____

    _____

    _____

    _____

2. Jesus summed up the Ten Commandments in just
    two. Read Matthew 22:37-39 and write how you
    could apply this on a daily basis.

    _____

    _____

    _____

    _____

3. The best description of *agape* love is perfectly written in 1 Corinthians 13:4-7. Using this passage, make a list of love do's and don'ts.

LOVE DO'S   LOVE DON'TS

_____   _____
_____   _____
_____   _____
_____   _____
_____   _____

4. John 3:16 speaks of God's great love for you that He willingly gave His most prized possession as payment for your sins. Write a prayer thanking the Lord for this.

_____
_____
_____
_____

5. In Deuteronomy 5 Moses gave the Ten Command-ments to the children of Israel. Summed up in Romans 13:10, what is the fulfillment of these laws?

_____
_____
_____
_____

6. Titus 2:4 teaches the kind of love God wants you to have for your husband, children, and other people in your life. What are the ways you can demonstrate *phileo* love to others?

_____ _____

_____ _____

_____ _____

_____ _____

7. Write the *phileo* love found in these Scriptures and share what they mean to you.

a. Romans 12:10

_____

_____

b. Titus 3:14

_____

_____

c. 1 Peter 1:22

_____

_____

8. Just as loving qualities can spread to others, unloving ones can too. Read Hebrews 12:15 and write what you learn.

_____

_____

_____

_____

9. Once you learn what unloving attitudes can do, God shares the correction. Read Psalm 139:23-24 and write what you should do.

    _____

    _____

    _____

    _____

10. Forgiveness is not optional. As you read the example of forgiveness in Acts 7:55-60, why do you think Stephen reacted this way?

    _____

    _____

    _____

    _____

11. Submissiveness is also a loving quality. Study 1 Peter 3:1 and share why this is important to all women.

    _____

    _____

    _____

    _____

12. It's important to understand genuine love in order to reflect God's love to others. Disclose what the Lord has personally taught you in this chapter.

    _____

    _____

    _____

    _____

And now abide faith, hope, love, these three; but the greatest of these is love.

                                        - 1 Corinthians 13:13

PRAYERS & NOTES

_____

_____

_____

_____

_____

_____

_____

_____

_____

_____

_____

_____

_____

_____

_____

_____

_____

_____

_____

Prayers & Notes

_____

_____

_____

_____

_____

_____

_____

_____

_____

_____

_____

_____

_____

_____

_____

_____

_____

8

SHE IS A FRIEND

1. God has created friendship relationships and He has called you to be His friend. Read the following Scriptures and explain them in your own words.

    a. Exodus 33:11

    _____

    _____

    b. 2 Chronicles 20:7

    _____

    _____

    c. John 15:15

    _____

    _____

2. Loyalty is essential in friendships. What does loyalty mean to you? Do you think the members of your family sense you are loyal to them?

_____

_____

_____

_____

_____

3. Marriage should be the closest friendship a woman can have. Read Proverbs 31:11. Whether you are married or not, what do you think this verse means in terms of loyalty and friendship?

_____

_____

_____

_____

_____

4. A good friend is someone who has proven to be a good and sympathetic listener. Write out the following Scriptures and commit to applying these principles to your friendships.

   a. Proverbs 10:19

_____

_____

   b. James 1:19

_____

_____

5. When you care for others and live out the truth of 1 Corinthians 12:26, you are a woman who reflects God. Think of some specific ways you can put this kind of caring into action for your close friendships.

_____

_____

_____

_____

6. Read Proverbs 17:22. Think about how much better you can reflect God's love through laughter than through irritable and cranky behavior. How can God use you to bring more fun to the ones you love?

_____

_____

_____

_____

7. Unfortunately, many times we find it easier to criticize than to express approval. How can you show praise and appreciation to your family and friends?

_____

_____

_____

_____

8. If you want to be a friend, be flexible. Are there areas in your relationships where you refuse to bend? If so, commit these to the Lord and ask Him to soften you.

_____

_____

_____

_____

9. God has made us different and we are all works in progress. How can Philippians 1:6 help you to be more accepting and patient with your friends?

_____

_____

_____

_____

10. List two reasons why it is important to be a loving, friendly reflection of God.

_____

_____

_____

_____

11. What reward is found in Proverbs 31:28, 30 if you are the kind of friend God wants you to be?

_____

_____

_____

_____

12. Take a moment to assess your relationships. How can you improve to be a better friend that reflects God?

_____

_____

_____

_____

No longer do I call you servants, for a servant does not know what his master is doing; but I have called you friends.

- John 15:15

PRAYERS & NOTES

_____

_____

_____

_____

_____

_____

_____

_____

_____

_____

_____

_____

_____

_____

_____

_____

_____

Prayers & Notes

SHE IS OBEDIENT

1. Throughout the Bible, we're admonished to obey God. Read the following Scriptures and record the instruction and the blessing that awaits you if you listen and obey.

   a. Deuteronomy 12:28

   _____

   _____

   b. Psalm 119:165

   _____

   _____

   c. Proverbs 8:32-34

   _____

   _____

2. When you obey God you are an effective witness to the world. Read Philippians 2:12-16 and look for ways you can eagerly obey and note the blessing that is promised to follow.

_____

_____

_____

_____

3. If you're single, widowed or divorced, Isaiah 54:5 says "the LORD is your husband." What are some ways you can walk in obedience to God, regardless of your marital status?

_____

_____

_____

_____

4. Another word for obedience is submission. Read Ephesians 5:21-24 and write how this applies to you.

_____

_____

_____

_____

5. Examine 1 Timothy 2:12-14. After thinking about these verses, how do they help you to understand the protection of obedience?

_____

_____

_____

_____

6. Obedience to some Scriptures in the Bible can seem fearful if you don't understand them. After reading 1 Peter 3:5-6, how is Sarah an example to you?

_____

_____

_____

_____

7. Titus 2:5 tells us to be "obedient to our husbands that the Word of God may not be blasphemed." What behavior would misrepresent God to the world?

_____

_____

_____

_____

8. In reviewing Ephesians 5:22-33, God designed marriage as the symbol of Christ's redemption. How are these verses relevant to you in order to reflect God to others?

_____

_____

_____

_____

_____

9. Describe the obedient Proverbs 31 woman in your own words.

_____

_____

_____

_____

10. Explain how the following Scriptures are helpful to you to be a woman who obeys the Lord.

a. Deuteronomy 6:5-6

_____

_____

b. Ecclesiastes 12:13

_____

_____

c. Luke 6:46

_____

_____

d. John 14:21

_____

_____

e. 1 John 2:4

_____

_____

f. 1 John 5:3

_____

_____

Do all things without complaining and disputing, that you may become blameless and harmless, children of God without fault in the midst of a crooked and perverse generation, among whom you shine as lights in the world, holding fast the word of life.

- Philippians 2:14-16

Prayers & Notes

Prayers & Notes

10

SHE KEEPS
HER HOME

1. As women of God, we are called to be keepers of the home. What does it mean to keep your home? Jot down some things that come to your mind.

_____

_____

_____

_____

2. It is each woman's choice to marry or not. After reading 1 Corinthians 7:34, biblically speaking, what is the advantage of the woman who decides not to marry?

_____

_____

_____

_____

3. If you do decide to marry, you should desire to please your husband. What are some things listed in Titus 2:4-5 that reflects the behavior of a homemaker?

_____ _____
_____ _____
_____ _____

4. Some women feel they don't have enough time to attend to the needs of her home. According to Proverbs 31:27, what is one sure way to accomplish what you need to do?

_____
_____
_____
_____

5. Meditate on the term "eat the bread of idleness." Is there an area in your life that falls under that description? Write down anything that is stealing your time and commit it to the Lord.

_____
_____
_____
_____

6. We can see if the physical needs of our home are being met, but the emotional needs are less obvious. What kind of atmosphere are you setting for your home? Really search your heart for your answer.

_____
_____
_____
_____

7. Proverbs 11:16 reads, "A kindhearted woman gains respect." Do you want to be known as a kind and tenderhearted woman? Read Romans 12:2 and consider some ways you can live out this verse in your home.

_____

_____

_____

_____

_____

8. When you're under the pressure of keeping your home, it is easy to get frustrated, to complain, or blurt out gruff comments. Read the following Scriptures and comment on the kind of woman you want to be.

   a. Proverbs 31:26

   _____

   _____

   b. Colossians 3:12

   _____

   _____

9. If you're responsible for children, you have an incredible amount of influence on them—and sometimes you need to remind yourself to have patience with them. For help in this area, write out what the exhortation found in 1 Thessalonians 5:14 means to you.

_____

_____

_____

_____

10. Whether you are a full-time homemaker or work outside the home, what is the most important guideline to keep in mind about your priorities? Read Matthew 6:33 to assist you.

_____

_____

_____

_____

11. Sometimes women perceive homemaking as tiring and dreary, but what does Galatians 6:9 guarantee? How can this help you to reflect God in keeping your home?

_____

_____

_____

_____

12. Do you want your home to be a place where people find hope, healing and love? You can be a blessing to your family by following the admonitions found in 1 Peter 3:8-9. List them here.

_____

_____

_____

_____

_____

She watches over the ways of her household, and does not eat the bread of idleness.

- Proverbs 31:27

PRAYERS & NOTES

Prayers & Notes

C H A P T E R

11

SHE IS AN INTERCESSOR

1. The woman who reflects God is an intercessor. In your own words, describe the characteristics and traits of a woman who intercedes for others.

_____

_____

_____

_____

2. Read the story of Abigail in 1 Samuel 25:2-11. In verse 3 it says Abigail had good understanding. Why do you think good understanding is necessary to be an intercessor for others?

_____

_____

_____

_____

3. How does this account in 1 Samuel 25 describe Abigail's husband, Nabal? Why aren't Nabal's traits desirable for one who wants to be an intercessor?

_____

_____

_____

_____

4. An intercessor is alert to danger. As you read 1 Samuel 25:12-20, you see Abigail's actions when she saw danger threatening her home. What actions can you take to keep danger out of your home?

_____

_____

_____

_____

5. A woman who intercedes for others is wise. Read the following Scriptures and find the wise attributes that Abigail displayed in 1 Samuel 25:23-28.

   a. Proverbs 15:1

_____

_____

   b. Proverbs 29:23

_____

_____

   c. James 4:6

_____

_____

6. Standing in the gap and praying for her loved ones was one of Abigail's examples as an intercessor. What are some things you can be standing in the gap and praying for your family and friends right now?

    _____

    _____

    _____

    _____

7. Read how Abigail proved her knowledge of the Lord in 1 Samuel 25:29-31. Write some of the things she said from these verses that reveals her knowledge of God—qualifying her to be an intercessor for others.

    _____

    _____

    _____

    _____

8. As an intercessor, what kind of knowledge would be important for you to be able to intercede for others?

    _____

    _____

    _____

    _____

9. Abigail waited for God's deliverance and didn't take matters into her own hands. How could a woman who intercedes for others wait for God's deliverance?

    _____

    _____

    _____

    _____

10. In 1 Samuel 25:32-40 we read the conclusion to Abigail's intercession for her family. What was her response in verse 41?

_____

_____

_____

_____

11. Humility is one of the most important aspects to have as an intercessor. Read John 13:12-17 and note what the Lord has revealed to you.

_____

_____

_____

_____

12. Abigail succeeded in interceding for her family and kept her household safe. Is your household safe because of your intercession? Write a prayer asking the Holy Spirit to help you to become an intercessor.

_____

_____

_____

_____

Then she arose, bowed her face to the earth, and said, "Here is your maidservant, a servant to wash the feet of the servants of my lord."

- 1 Samuel 25:41

Prayers & Notes

_____

_____

_____

_____

_____

_____

_____

_____

_____

_____

_____

_____

_____

_____

_____

_____

_____

Prayers & Notes

12

SHE NURTURES THE YOUNG

1. God has given you nurturing abilities for children. List the children (of all ages) who are under your influence—even if you don't have children, think of some you could bless.

   _____
   _____
   _____
   _____

2. Prayer shows love to a child, especially if they are older and live far away. Write a prayer for the children in your life, and commit to praying for them daily.

   _____
   _____
   _____
   _____

3. Never underestimate the power of planting seeds in the children God has put in your life. Explore some ways you can teach children about the Lord and list them here.

_____

_____

_____

_____

4. You can open up the world to children by "strewing pretty things in their path." Name some of these things that would be a reflection of God.

_____

_____

_____

_____

5. Sometimes we restrict children more than necessary. Read Mark 10:13-16 and describe what you see.

_____

_____

_____

_____

6. It's easy to get frustrated and short-tempered with children. Write out and memorize Galatians 5:22-23. Ask God to help you in those trying times.

_____

_____

_____

_____

7. It is our responsibility to guide and correct children. What do these Scriptures teach about discipline?

a. Proverbs 13:24

_____

_____

b. Hebrews 12:5-6

_____

_____

8. There is a definite difference between discipline and abuse. Read Ephesians 6:4 and Colossians 3:21. What is the result of being too harsh on a child?

_____

_____

_____

9. Children need to know you are delighted in them. How can these verses help you to reflect God?

a. Romans 14:19

_____

_____

b. 1 Thessalonians 5:11

_____

_____

c. Hebrews 3:13

_____

_____

10. Are you overcome with worry for your children? The Lord wants you to put away worry and depend on Him. What does He tell you in Isaiah 41:10?

_____

_____

_____

_____

11. The most important thing you can do for children is to love them. You can never love too much. What do these Scriptures share about love?

a. John 13:34

_____

_____

b. 1 Thessalonians 3:12

_____

_____

c. 1 Peter 4:8

_____

_____

d. 1 John 4:7

_____

_____

Whoever receives one of these little children in My name receives Me; and whoever receives Me, receives not Me but Him who sent Me.

- Mark 9:37

Prayers & Notes

_____

_____

_____

_____

_____

_____

_____

_____

_____

_____

_____

_____

_____

_____

_____

Prayers & Notes

13

SHE INSPIRES OTHERS

1. Judges 2:16-19 describes a dark time in Israel when the nation was involved in idolatry, mirroring our society today. During this time, God raised up Deborah to inspire the Israelites. What do we know about her from reading Judges 4:4-5?

_____

_____

_____

_____

2. Like Deborah, how can the Lord use you to inspire and comfort people around you?

_____

_____

_____

3. It would have been easy for Deborah to listen to the people's complaints and criticize the soldiers. Instead, how did Deborah inspire and encourage Barak in Judges 4:6-9?

_____

_____

_____

_____

4. When you inspire others, it is like breathing life into them. In what ways can you inspire others in difficult circumstances?

_____

_____

_____

_____

5. You can also be a negative inspiration to the people around you. How might you be discouraging?

_____

_____

_____

_____

6. Deborah was able to offer encouragement because she trusted God. We gain courage when we realize God is with us. Personalize the promise in Joshua 1:9 and write it here.

_____

_____

_____

_____

7. Proverbs 31:11 says, "The heart of her husband safely trusts her." Read the following Scriptures and note how can you establish credibility and inspire your loved ones to trust you.

   a. Matthew 5:16

   _____

   _____

   b. Romans 12:17

   _____

   _____

   c. 2 Corinthians 8:21

   _____

   _____

8. We can inspire others when we meditate on God's Word. What are the promises in Psalm 1:1-3 for those who do? List them here.

   _____

   _____

   _____

   _____

9. In order to be an inspiration to others, you must be fully committed to God. What did Jesus say about being committed to our King in Luke 9:23?

   _____

   _____

   _____

   _____

10. In Judges 5:1-31, Deborah sang praises for God's victory, inspiring others to do the same. Read 2 Corinthians 2:14-15 and write how you can inspire others when you give thanks to God.

_____

_____

_____

_____

11. To be a spiritual inspiration to others, you must be a doer of the Word. Read Ezekiel 33:30-33 and comment on what you learn.

_____

_____

_____

12. It doesn't matter if you're young or old, a career woman or a stay-at-home mom, God wants to use you to influence and inspire His people. Write a prayer asking the Lord to show you how you can be an inspiration to others.

_____

_____

_____

_____

Be strong and of good courage; do not be afraid, nor be dismayed, for the LORD your God is with you wherever you go.

~ Joshua 1:9

Prayers & Notes

Prayers & Notes

CHAPTER

14

SHE KNOWS
HER PROTECTOR

1. In order to be bold about sharing your faith, you need
    to know that God is your Protector. Write out 1 Peter
    3:12 to remind yourself who is on your side.

    _____
    _____
    _____
    _____

2. As you read 1 Peter 4:12-14, describe the adversity you
    face or have faced personally in regard to your faith
    and note how God has protected and blessed you.

    _____
    _____
    _____
    _____

3. If you are going to let your light shine to reflect God, ridicule and persecution cannot be avoided. What protection is found in these Scriptures?

    a. Matthew 5:10-12

    _____

    _____

    b. Romans 8:16-17

    _____

    _____

4. First Peter 5:8 gives a vivid description of Satan's intentions towards you. In 1 Peter 3:15, how can you be protected from being fearful of Satan?

    _____

    _____

    _____

5. Isaiah 8:12-13 confirms God's protection saying, "Fear not the enemy. Sanctify the Lord of Hosts—let Him be your dread." What does this mean to you?

    _____

    _____

    _____

    _____

6. Isaiah 8:14 promises God will be your sanctuary. Define what a sanctuary is to you.

    _____

    _____

    _____

    _____

7. Sanctification is important for God's protection. List some ways to sanctify or set apart your life to God.

_____

_____

_____

_____

_____

8. In times of crisis and danger, we need to rely on our Protector, our Rock. Write out Proverbs 18:10 and commit it to memory to recall in times of need.

_____

_____

_____

_____

9. Observe the transformation which took place in Peter's life—from terror (Luke 22:54-60) to boldness (Acts 5:26-32). Why was he no longer fearful?

_____

_____

_____

_____

10. Read what Peter and the disciples prayed in response to persecution in Acts 4:29-31. Write this prayer in your own words for boldness in your witness.

_____

_____

_____

_____

11. The Psalms are filled with reminders that God is our Rock and our Fortress of protection. Search the following verses and note what they say.

a. Psalm 31:3

_____

_____

b. Psalm 57:1

_____

_____

c. Psalm 61:2

_____

_____

d. Psalm 63:7

_____

_____

12. Meditate on what Jesus did for you on the cross. He gave His life so you could live without fear. Share your gratitude to Him for being your Protector and Lord.

_____

_____

_____

_____

_____

He only is my rock and my salvation; He is my defense; I shall not be moved. In God is my salvation and my glory; The rock of my strength, and my refuge is in God.

~ Psalm 62:6-7

PRAYERS & NOTES

Prayers & Notes

CHAPTER

15

SHE IS CONTENT

1. Think for a moment what life was like for Eve (Genesis 2:8-25; 3:1-7). She lived in a place of beauty and perfection, yet she was discontent. What led to her discontentment?

   _____

   _____

   _____

   _____

2. If Eve had nurtured a thankful heart for the things God had given her, she wouldn't have listened to the serpent's lies. How can you develop a thankful heart?

   _____

   _____

   _____

   _____

3. When the world witnesses a contented person, they see something they are lacking. How could your contentment offer the world an accurate reflection of God?

_____

_____

_____

_____

4. Satan's presentation can sound much more reasonable and sensible than God's way. Read 2 Corinthians 10:4-5 and write down what God commands us to do in order to be content.

_____

_____

_____

_____

5. Satan always opposes God's plan and does whatever he can to lure you away from contentment. What are some things you can do to stay in God's plan?

_____

_____

_____

_____

6. Just as Satan deceived Eve, he deceived some in the Corinthian church—this is why we need to stand firmly on God's Word. What happens when we don't? See 2 Corinthians 11:2-3.

_____

_____

_____

7. When you have the "Eve mentality"—thinking you know better than God—you are discontent. What warning is given in 1 Corinthians 10:12?

_____

_____

_____

_____

8. Like Eve, the moment you indulge in your own will, you will lose paradise. Your paradise is your relationship with Father God. Think for a few moments what that means and note your reaction.

_____

_____

_____

_____

9. When you become discontent and stop obeying God, you've placed yourself on the throne of your life—and the love of the world has crept in. What do these Scriptures teach you?

   a. Romans 12:2

   _____

   _____

   b. James 4:4

   _____

   _____

   c. 1 John 2:15-17

   _____

   _____

   _____

10. So many people destroy their witness because they had the "Eve mentality." What is the solution to discontentment found in Mark 8:34?

_____

_____

_____

_____

11. It isn't easy to give up your fleshly desires and dethrone yourself—you need God's Spirit to empower you. What does Galatians 5:16-18 say about this?

_____

_____

_____

_____

12. As we conclude this study, write a prayer of gratefulness to God for the transforming work the Holy Spirit has begun in you to become a woman who reflects God.

_____

_____

_____

_____

_____

Now godliness with contentment is great gain.

~ 1 Timothy 6:6

Prayers & Notes

Prayers & Notes

Prayers & Notes

Prayers & Notes

Prayers & Notes

Prayers & Notes